Reconceptualising dementia

Amelesia not dementia – unmindfulness not madness

A manifesto

Mina Drever

BA, PGCE, PhD

AMELESIA
BOOKS

First published 2022 in the United Kingdom
by MinaDrever Limited

ISBN 978-1-7397900-0-4 (print)
ISBN 978-1-7397900-1-1 (ebook)

A catalogue record for this book is available from the British
Library

Printed in the United Kingdom

Design and layout by Daisy Editorial

Cover image by Lidiya Oleandra/Shutterstock.com

Contents

To reconceptualise dementia we must:

- abolish the word dementia and adopt Amelesia – a 'much kinder word'
- stop saying that people with mental decline are not the person they used to be
- rethink the concept of time and space
- learn to communicate with Amelesians.

Preface

Amelesia not dementia – unmindfulness not madness

I have been thinking about dementia for well over twenty years now and I have become increasingly concerned at how a condition that affects us mostly (but not exclusively) as we[1] get older is being sensationalised.

The headlines are frightening and very disturbing:

- Millions with eye conditions at higher risk of dementia – *The Guardian* 21-Sep-2021
- Widespread pain may be an early warning of dementia – *The Times* 17-Aug-2021
- Someone gets dementia every three minutes – Facebook headline by the Alzheimer's Society (March 2020)
- Boy, 4, with dementia has forgotten how to say 'Mama' – *The Times* 26-Apr-2018

[1] In this book, 'we' is used as an all-inclusive address to all readers.

- Dementia now causing one in eight deaths – *The Times* 07-Aug-2019, Greg Hurst, social affairs editor (statistics from the Office for National Statistics)
- High blood pressure causes dementia – https://healthline.com
- There are over one hundred types of dementia – https://trinityhomecare.co.uk

I started questioning this 'dementia' in the late twentieth century, when my mother was diagnosed with vascular dementia in her mid seventies. So many questions crowded my mind that I thought I would explode.

- What is dementia?
- What is vascular dementia?
- Why is everybody treating my mum as if she is stupid?
- Why can't they just accept what she is saying, even if it is wrong?
- Why can't they see that she gets upset when they ask her 'Have you forgotten already? I just told you!'
- Why did the doctor say that we have to accept that she is not our mother any more?
- Why is she being dismissed like a naughty child who doesn't know how to participate in a conversation?
- Why do carers talk down to her?
- Why can't she just pay attention? (I could read this in their exasperated sighs.)

I started venting my anger and frustration onto paper. A few years later, after she had suffered these humiliations for over a decade and after she had died disappointed with her family for having 'abandoned her', a memoir emerged in which I endeavoured to give the credibility to the last ten years of my mother's life that she would have wanted.

It is difficult to express in words exactly what I mean. She wanted to be believed. She wanted her desires and wishes to be granted. She wanted to be respected for knowing what she wanted to choose and decide. By herself. For herself. If she believed that night was day and day was night, it mattered to her. Why did the people around her not believe her? And why did they tease her about her mistaken reality?

The first paragraph of the memoir,[2] which I eventually published, encapsulates succinctly what I thought of how my mother was perceived by other people and, consequently, how she was spoken to and how she was treated:

> They say that your mother has gone. They say 'she is not your mother any more ... The disease has taken over her mind ... The dementia has disconnected her from her rationality ...' But this is not so. Angela never stopped being the person that she had been. Right to the end of her last breath she never stopped thinking about other people and their needs ... The past and the present became one ... Time and space were unified in the reality of remembered episodes, bursts of memories that presented themselves to her mind in cinematic snapshots.

---

[2] Mina Drever (2017). *Thank You Lady*. Austin Macauley Publishers, London.

Since this memoir was written, my theories have been reinforced by my voluntary work as a visitor to Redbond Lodge residential care home in Great Dunmow (Essex). I sit and chat with people whose mental abilities have been affected by some sort of damage caused by obscure disturbances in their brains. Many of them have been diagnosed with 'dementia'. As they tell me stories of their lives, the people they like to sit with and why they prefer certain television programmes to others, I get to know each individual's character. I can imagine clearly the tolerant mother, the fiercely proud civil servant, the fun-loving sailor, the proud business man, the patriotic resistance fighter of the Second World War, the dedicated community gardener, the passionate music teacher.

I am more convinced now than I was when I started writing my memoir about my mother's life during her 'dementia' years that when our minds become impaired by some brain disease that we cannot see, we do not stop being the person that we used to be. Our minds wander freely, without any conscious control on our part, between historical and present events.

Because people listening to our mental meanderings do not know our past, they assume that we do not know what we are talking about. If we confuse the person in front of us with someone from our past, they assume that we no longer know the important people in our lives. But we just cannot remember. Sometimes we cannot find the right words. But we know what we want to say, if only the appropriate words would come to our lips, and if only 'they', those listening to us, would just give us the time to think!

Do you remember what it feels like to try to speak in a foreign language when words from your first language jostle for supremacy over the alien phrases that rush to the periphery of your memory bank? I sometimes can almost see the brains of the people I speak with in the care home working in this way. I can certainly feel them as they pierce me with their eyes as if to say 'Just give me a moment ...'

This frustration and these questions over the years have developed into a desire to revolutionise the way we envisage the minds of people affected by dementia and our relationships with them. To help us do that I have formulated the following statement of four intents.

1. **Abolish the term 'dementia'** – a most insulting word, dementia is a label that has done enormous psychological damage to relationships between those with brains affected by a number of different physical conditions (such as Alzheimer's and Lewy body) and those with healthy brains; it has disempowered entire families, as well as professionals; it has diminished the very essence of the person.

2. **Adopt the word Amelesia** – I constructed this term from two Greek words: *Ameles* means unmindfulness and the suffix –*sia* means the condition or state in which we find ourselves. Amelesia describes perfectly where the damaged brain is: elsewhere, anywhere but 'here' and 'now'.

3. **Recognise the permanence of the core inner person** – our inner core self remains for others to reach out to despite the increasing absence of coherence when communicating our most basic of needs, never mind our more esoteric thoughts and dreams.

4. **Reconceptualise time and space in the disabled mind**
   – the decreasing ability of our working memory to stay
   'in the moment' and the increasing tendency of our mind
   to meander and wander into the time and space of our
   collective life experiences, in order to make sense of
   what is happening 'now', leads to a fusion of time and
   space in our mind.

These goals are realistic and can be achieved. The paths have
already been laid by numerous people. My aim is to tap into
the voices that have spoken before me to show you, firstly,
that the time has come to be brave and courageous in going
against the grain and, secondly, that it is perfectly possible to
do this in a constructive way.

With this manifesto I explain my four intents in some detail,
what I can present in their support and how I hope to alter our
perception of dementia. I will start with an introduction to these
intents and why I consider it necessary to reconceptualise
dementia.

Statement of intents

To reconceptualise dementia, we must change our mindsets. We must think of this condition in a completely different way. To do that we must change the language that we use:

1. **Abolish the word dementia.**
2. **Stop saying that the person that we knew 'has gone'.**
3. **Rethink the concept of time and space in the disabled mind.**
4. **Learn how to sustain meaningful conversations with Amelesians.**

These intents are driven by passionate concern for what I see as gross injustice in the way we talk about people who have been diagnosed with 'dementia' and consequently the way we talk **to** them and **with** them.

I have known someone living with dementia. My mother. I am also a linguist. I have studied language and I have taught language. A lifetime of this work has taught me that the precise use of language is paramount in establishing mutually meaningful and satisfying conversations between two or more people. At the social level a good and satisfying conversation is one that makes us feel good about ourselves. This implies that we have not felt judged or ridiculed or put down by the other person. Sadly, many people diagnosed with dementia feel quite the opposite.

Speaking anecdotally, this is very common. I am a volunteer visitor to a residential care home. I observe well-meaning carers literally lost for words in the presence of seemingly irrational arguments who end up saying the wrong thing, which upsets the residents towards whom they mean no harm.

I want to change that. I want to give families and professionals the opportunity to learn a different way of speaking to people displaying symptoms associated with diseases that affect mental capabilities.

There are thousands of professional people worldwide engaged in the work of unpacking the many aspects of all the diseases that come under the umbrella name of dementia. My work is a contribution to that global endeavour. I am presenting here an idea that has been tried out by a small group of students and by one ordinary citizen and that is supported heartily by the manager of one residential care home.

This small group of people – who felt the same way as I do, who believed and trusted in me and wanted to try out my ideas – now want everybody to join in a worldwide shift of mindsets.

Why do we need to reconceptualise dementia?

Because the stigma persists. Many people around the world[3] are involved in destigmatising dementia. But it is not working. Professor Tom Kitwood was a pioneer in England and dedicated his professional and personal life to taking the veil off the face of this frightening condition. He has partially succeeded. His work is being continued at pace by his former student – and now Professor of Dementia Studies at the University of Worcester – Dawn Brooker, who has expanded on Kitwood's person-centred approach to dementia care and developed the VIPS framework with detailed guidelines on exactly what this approach looks like.[4]

According to Professor Brooker and her academic colleagues who are continuing Kitwood's formidable attack on what he called the 'malignant social psychology', there is much to be done to achieve his ultimate goal, which is that we, society, you and me, adopt a 'benign' attitude towards people living with dementia (see Kitwood, Brooker 2019).

Governments and influential bodies such as the World Health Organization (WHO) are paying a lot of attention to these voices of despair and they are listening to professional experts, as well as to people living with Alzheimer's and similar conditions,

---

[3] For a comprehensive list see Afterword on p 178 of Tom Kitwood, Dawn Brooker (ed.) (2019). *Dementia Reconsidered, Revisited: The person still comes first.* Open University Press.

[4] Briefly, VIPS stands for Value-based Individual approach to understanding the Perspective of the person needing support in a Social environment that supports psychological needs. Full explanation on page 175 of Dawn Brooker, Isabelle Latham (2016). *Person-centred Dementia Care: Making services better with the VIPS framework.* 2nd edition. Jessica Kingsley Publishers, London.

in order to change societal attitudes towards these conditions and, more crucially, towards people living with them.

In 2013 the G8 held a first international summit on dementia at the highest political level. A number of crucial declarations were made to harmonise work in this area, including the necessity of reducing the stigma associated with this condition:

> 27. Addressing stigma and ensuring that people with dementia are treated with dignity and respect are critical. We therefore commend the creation of the UN Independent Expert on the enjoyment of all human rights by older persons and we ask that the perspective of older people affected by dementia is integrated into their work.

> 28. Civil society is also well placed to play a major role in changing public attitudes. Therefore, we agreed to call on civil society to continue and to enhance global efforts to reduce stigma, exclusion and fear.[5]

In England, the Prime Minister's Challenge on Dementia initiative (set up by the former Prime Minister David Cameron in 2010)[6] has been gathering momentum across the country with numerous actions.

The National Health Service in England has produced professional training standards in order to reduce the stigma

---

[5] http://www.g8.utoronto.ca/healthG8/2013-dementia-declaration.html
[6] Department of Health (2015). *Prime Minister's Challenge on Dementia 2020*. https://www.gov.uk/government/publications/prime-ministers-challenge-on-dementia-2020

associated with dementia[7] and the Six Cs Model of dementia nursing: care, compassion, competence, communication, courage and commitment. NICE (National Institute for Health and Care Excellence) has published guidelines.[8] Under the umbrella terms 'living well' and 'supporting well' many programmes have been set up across the country since 2010 by local authorities, independent charities, universities, and small and large voluntary groups to plan for and provide person-centred social care.

Universities now conduct a great variety of studies on dementia, including higher degrees leading to masters and doctorates. All this is being done in the name of reducing stigma. Because only when stigma is removed can the condition be viewed in a different light.

The UK government spearheaded a concerted international effort at the G8 Dementia Summit in December 2013 and many national and international bodies were set up to establish research and social programmes to eradicate the stigma associated with this condition. The International Dementia Institute was set up in London. The Global Dementia Action Alliance and the World Dementia Council were born.

---

[7] Skills for Health, Health Education England, Skills for Care (2018). Dementia Training Standards Framework. https://www.skillsforhealth. org.uk/services/item/176-dementia-core-skills-education-and-training-framework

[8] NICE (National Institute for Health and Care Excellence (June 2018). Dementia assessment, management and support for people living with dementia and their carers. https://www.nice.org.uk/search?q=dementia+

The OECD (Organisation for Economic Development) has produced a roadmap for dementia to coordinate post-diagnosis support as well as policies for diagnosis, treatment and prevention across countries.

In 2018 the WHO published a dementia plan for 2017–2025. One of its ambitions is to 'reduce stigma'.[9]

The WHO has listed all the diseases and brain damage events implicated in the decline of cognitive functions[10] such as planning events, reasoning arguments, recalling experiences, and recognising people and spaces.

Novels and memoirs are creating powerful witnesses to this condition that is sweeping humanity at an alarming rate. *Still Alice* by Lisa Genova[11] is a brilliantly written novel (turned into an award-winning film and a poignant play) that draws us into Alice's own awareness of what is happening to her mind and at the same time her powerlessness to do anything to stop it invading her very existence. *Elisabeth is Missing* by Emma Healey[12] (dramatised for the BBC with the amazing portrayal of Maud by Glenda Jackson, broadcast on 08-Dec-2019) gives a window into 'normal' people's dismissal of an elderly woman's wanderings through her past life, seemingly a made-up-past with no connections to her present. There is a cruel lack of even

---

[9] WHO (2018). Towards a dementia plan: a WHO guide. https://www.who.int/publications/i/item/towards-a-dementia-plan-a-who-guide

[10] WHO (June 2018). ICD-11 (International Classification of Diseases) https://icd.who.int/icdapi

[11] Lisa Genova (2007). *Still Alice*. Simon & Schuster, London.

[12] Emma Healey (2014). *Elisabeth is Missing*. Penguin Random House, London.

respectful doubt on the part of friends and family that there might be some grain of truth in what she is trying to convey.

Ordinary people have courageously allowed others to enter their inner 'dementia' world by speaking about what it feels like to be diagnosed with early onset Alzheimer's and by becoming ambassadors for the Alzheimer's Society. Wendy Mitchell has written movingly and clearly about her experiences in her memoir *Somebody I Used to Know*.[13] Keith Oliver, a former headteacher diagnosed with early onset Alzheimer's, has contributed to the work started by Professor Kitwood by joining the discussion – in *Dementia Reconsidered, Revisited* edited by Professor Dawn Brooker – on how best to enlighten the general public and professionals on what it feels like to live with Alzheimer's. Kate Swaffer co-founded Dementia Alliance International in Australia for the global community of people living with dementia and travels the world to show us that this condition does not mean the end of life as we know it.

Despite these developments, I do not see much change on the ground in how people living with reduced mental capacities as a result of the array of conditions listed by bodies such as the WHO are perceived. Yes, there is awareness of the importance of 'showing respect' and a great deal of emphasis is placed on preserving 'dignity'. But respect and dignity are interpreted very narrowly, more as practical activities – gentle handling of and ensuring privacy for residents in care homes living with Alzheimer's – rather than thinking of them as people with functioning brains (albeit damaged brains) capable of

---

[13] Wendy Mitchell (2018). *Somebody I Used to Know*. Bloomsbury, London.

expressing opinions, desires and emotions such as anger as a result of the way carers might speak to them.

I believe that these attitudes will persist until the word dementia is taken out of our societal discourse.

Too much is excused in the name of dementia.

Many people are shying away from abandoning the word dementia. There is a reluctance to be courageous. Why? Is it because it is convenient? Maybe because everybody is used to it? Because it is familiar? Because it is entrenched in our psyche?

Do we want to change our concept of dementia? If yes, let us:

- ▸ stop using the word dementia
- ▸ stop treating people with mental decline as if they are mad and stupid
- ▸ stop talking down to them.

Abolish the word dementia – let us adopt the word Amelesia

Dementia = madness; Amelesia = unmindfulness

If we have to have a word to describe symptoms that are common to a myriad of diseases caused by structural and/or chemical damage in the brain then let us adopt Amelesia, a 'much kinder word' as suggested by Sue King, the manager at Redbond Lodge residential care home in Great Dunmow.[14]

> I really love the wording chosen instead of using dementia. Amelesia is a much kinder word. It would be lovely to use it worldwide and stop the stigma associated with dementia.

People have been looking for an alternative to the word dementia for some time now. Writing in *The Guardian* on 30 September 2017 Jason Corner asked: 'Dementia is a terrible

---

[14] The pilot study for the communicative approach to conversations with people affected by mental decline took place in Redbond Lodge care home.

word. Why do people still use it?' He went on to say that 'the word removes power from the person at the point of diagnosis and it has an impact on the stance of the people who interact with them'.

Also writing in *The Guardian*, a year earlier on 5 April 2016, Clare Allan questioned the way language is used in very disparaging terms when referring to states of mental health. She argued that 'misuse of language shapes attitudes and ... the impact is every bit as damaging as slurs attached to race or gender, sexuality or religion'.

The word dementia is used in our current times to refer to people who have been diagnosed with cognitive impairment, with reduced capacities to carry out mental discourse and operations as they used to do before brain damage occurred. I will talk about these conditions later. First, I want to focus on some words and phrases that are commonly used in English as alternative meanings for the Latin word *dementia*: madness and insanity; derangement of the mind; distraction and folly. I want to see if any of them apply to the people who are labelled with the word dementia. I have taken these meanings from the Free Dictionary.[15]

What are *madness and insanity*? Are they the same phenomenon or is there a marked difference between them? Yes and no. Socially we often use these words interchangeably. We will tease friends with 'you are totally insane' when they come up with a practical joke or a prank played at the expense

---

[15] www.thefreedictionary.com

of someone else. Or 'you must be mad' if they are about to embark on a dangerous adventure.

Insanity is used only in legal contexts in our modern times, in the sense that someone may have committed a crime as a result of a mental condition that rendered them 'not in control' of their actions. In medical diagnosis it is no longer used to describe psychiatric conditions such as bipolar disorder or schizophrenia.

There are so many meanings attached to the simple noun *madness* in English. There are countless explanations and definitions in the numerous dictionaries available online, often accompanied by very interesting examples of its use in literature over the ages, from Greek and Roman times to our present day. There is consensus, though, that madness denotes a myriad of behaviours that can be acceptable and not acceptable depending on the situation and on the people involved.

Derangement of mind suggests that something has upset the normal functioning of mental activities leading to unusual behaviours and to confusion, or simply to anger. This can happen to anyone and at any time and does not necessarily suggest a psychotic event, though it might. In other words, it can be a misleading term to describe the mind of someone who has been diagnosed with Alzheimer's, which is a physical condition in the brain.

Distraction is something that makes it difficult to pay attention or that draws attention away from familiar or everyday concerns; mental or emotional disturbance; agitation or confusion.

Folly suggests lack of good sense, understanding or foresight. One can talk of an act of folly; an act or instance of foolishness. We can all identify with the feeling of embarrassment when we remember our youthful follies.

The word dementia is made up of the Latin word *mens* – which means mind – and the Latin prefix *de* – which means down, away from, from, off, about, of, concerning, according to, with regard to.

The word mind in English has a vast array of connotations and usages. Do any of them apply to the people we know or meet who, we are told, have got dementia? Again using the definitions in the Free Dictionary, the word mind is defined as the 'faculty of a human or other animal by which it thinks, perceives, feels, remembers, or desires'. The word mind can be a synonym for many other words, such as reason and intention, planning and making judgements.

The healthy mind in a healthy brain is capable of countless mental abstract actions. It allows us to *reason* and gives us the power to make *intellectual* arguments through learning and understanding the world around us. Our mind helps us to make *judgements* about the viability of a situation and about people. We use our minds to *plan* a journey and to show what we *intend* to do. Sometimes we are in a good *frame of mind* to tackle something new; at other times we might lack the *courage* to face our own fears, whether we want to climb Everest or *speak our mind* about something that is taboo or dogma.

All these definitions and meanings raise questions: is the brain that is damaged by Alzheimer's or similar conditions capable of these mental acts or not? Are people labelled with a diagnosis of dementia capable of reasoning and making judgements? Can they no longer plan for themselves what they want to wear, where they want to go, what they want or do not want to eat? Are they 'mad'?

Are they mad?

In social interactions madness is a very derogatory term, and that is the problem with it. If you are mad you are behaving in a way that is not socially acceptable. In my search for how this word has been used over time, I came across this advice in the Free Dictionary:

> You should be careful which words you use to refer to someone who has an abnormal mental condition. The adjectives mad, insane, crazy, demented, and deranged, and the nouns lunatic, maniac, madman, and spastic are usually avoided nowadays in serious speech and writing because they are thought to be offensive. Instead you can say that someone is mentally ill. If their condition is less severe, you can say that they are mentally disturbed or unbalanced, or that they have psychological problems.[16]

I defy anyone to say that Maud (depicted by Glenda Jackson in the film) in the story *Elisabeth is Missing* is a *mad woman* just because she cannot explain, in words and verbal sequences used by the 'normal brain', why she is on her hands and knees digging a corner of a garden where she knows she has seen half of a make-up powder compact. She knows that it is the

---

[16] https://www.thefreedictionary.com/madness

missing piece that will lead to solving the mystery of her sister's death. But, because to everyone she appears to behave like a 'batty old woman' who does not know what she is doing or talking about (because of her Alzheimer's), the solution to the mystery takes a very long time to be found.

Who is to say that Maud is not capable of 'reasoning', just because we cannot follow her train of thought?

Someone I got to know quite well in 2016 in Redbond Lodge residential care home, who was bedbound, with a slowly deteriorating working memory, was incredibly interested in the process of Brexit. We had many discussions on the pros and cons of the political debates. She *judged* that, as she was going to die soon (said with a happy laughter and hope), she would take a neutral stance! But we had fun unpicking the *intellectual* arguments underpinning the pro-leave and the pro-remain positions.

As the inexorable train of my father-in-law's Alzheimer's progressed through the railways of his mind, I watched him meticulously *plan* his financial affairs. Okay, all the available surfaces in his bedroom were covered with stacks of notes and piles of coins, cheque books, notations on what each pile meant, bills and invoices to be sorted. Yes, he would lose the train of his thoughts and he would go over and over the whole thing again. Did that make him *mad*? *Demented*? *Stupid*? He knew what he *intended* to do with his money and his assets, even though he had 'forgotten' the processes and the sequential steps necessary to achieve his intentions.

Many of the residents who live in Redbond Lodge are often in angry and resentful frames of mind. They get frustrated at their hopelessness and helplessness. They often lash out to strike or hit the world around them, verbally and sometimes physically. But are they *mad? Demented? Stupid?*

I think it must take a certain kind of indefinable *courage* to accept dependence on the good nature of the people around us to ask for the most basic and intimate of help: 'Please, will you take me to the toilet? I am desperate. I don't want to wet myself.'

That is courage.

Therefore, if we agree that people diagnosed with 'dementia' are not mad, *let us stop the stigma associated with it by stopping using the word.*

Changing the name removes the stigma

Changing the name of a disease because of stigmas attached to certain terms is nothing new nor unusual. In fact, it is a desirable thing to do in order to influence medical treatments and policies that in some cases carry a disproportionate degree of bias, such as gout.[17] A study found that changing the name of the disease gout and referring to it by its medical term (UCA – urate crystal arthritis) was instrumental in destigmatising the condition, both medically and in the public perception of the

---

[17] Keith Petrie, Kate MacKrill, Christina Derksen, Nicola Dalbeth (2017). An illness by any other name: the effect of changing the disease label of gout on the perceptions of the illness and its management. https://acrabstracts.org/abstract/an-illness-by-any-other-name-the-effect-of-changing-the-disease-label-of-gout-on-the-perceptions-of-the-illness-and-its-management/

disease. Similar attitudinal changes were found among medical students who viewed a disease more seriously when a medical term was attached to it – myalgic encephalopathy (ME) rather than the more common label chronic fatigue syndrome.[18]

Another study with medical students found similarly interesting results: that a medical condition described using a common word can often be seen as less serious (and therefore less worthy of serious attention) than when the medical term is used.[19] An example is using impotence instead of erectile dysfunction disorder. An interesting essay on sexual health published in Australia suggests that 'case definitions are often used without due consideration of their implications and limitations'[20] in describing sexual health. This can have a damaging impact on how sexually transmitted diseases are dealt with, clinically and academically too.

This has implications for the word dementia versus the numerous names for all the different conditions that share similar symptoms, such as disorientation and memory loss. I have noticed in my volunteer work that carers, friends and family members talk of people with Alzheimer's or Lewy body in different ways, especially with different intonation and body

---

[18] Leonard Jason, Renee R Taylor, Sigita Plioplys, Zuzanna Stepanek, Jennifer Shlaes (2002). Evaluating attributions for an illness based upon the name: chronic fatigue syndrome, myalgic encephalopathy and Florence Nightingale disease. *American Journal of Community Psychology* 30(1): 133–148.

[19] Meredith E Young, Geoffrey R Norman, Karin R Humphreys (2008). The role of medical language in changing public perception of illness. *PLoS ONE* 3(12): e3875. https://doi.org/10.1371/journal.pone.0003875

[20] DJ Chan, B Donovan (2005). What's in a word? Case definitions in sexual health medicine. *International Journal of STD & Aids* 16: 91–94.

language, to the way they talk about residents with 'dementia'. The latter are literally dismissed because they are seen as not the same people and therefore not to be taken seriously, whereas the former are not responsible for their actions and words. It is not their fault. It is the disease, poor people! The studies suggest that a simple switch in terminology influences the way a disease is viewed by both the public and the medical professions and, ultimately, by policy makers at government level.

We no longer use terms such as hypochondria or manic depression, respectively known now as health anxiety and bipolar disorder. Spastic and crippled have been delegated to archaic dictionaries and handicapped people are more respectfully referred to as disabled. Those born with the condition Down syndrome used to be medically diagnosed as 'Mongolian idiots' and commonly known as Mongols. The very thought makes one cringe with embarrassment and shame. A documentary on the All 4 channel on British television (broadcast in November 2019) featured a number of young people with disabilities, including those with Down syndrome, who sought to lead independent lives, albeit in a well-supported environment. There was no indication or suggestion that these people were considered idiotic or unworthy of the same respect afforded to other young people with different disabilities in the programme. We have indeed come a long way from the not-so-distant days of mongolism. Let us make the same leap of imagination with people living with Alzheimer's and similar conditions.

So, it all comes down to language and how we use it. Let us start by asking ourselves what dementia is and what it is not, in the way it is used now in the twenty-first century. Then, let

us see what the word Amelesia means and why I suggest that
it reflects much better the way the damaged brain operates.

What is dementia? Is it a disease?

In his paper 'Should the word "dementia" be forgotten?'[21]
Jellinger says that:

> ... dementia is not a specific disorder or disease, but
> a description for a syndrome (group of symptoms)
> associated with loss of memory and other cognitive/
> intellectual functions that are severe enough to
> interfere with the tasks of daily life, lasting more
> than six months, but not present at birth, and not
> associated with loss of consciousness.

Before we go any further let us establish the difference between
a disease and a syndrome, according to differencebetween.
com:[22]

> A **syndrome** is the association of several clinically
> recognizable features. Any sickness or illness cannot
> be called a syndrome. A syndrome is a special case.
> This word is given to a set of symptoms that may
> occur altogether at once. The word 'syndrome' comes
> from the Greek meaning 'run together'. A syndrome
> cannot be traced down to a single cause because
> a set of symptoms may occur due to one disease or

---

[21] Kurt A Jellinger (October 2010). Should the word 'dementia' be
forgotten? *Journal of Cellular and Molecular Medicine* 14(10).
[22] https://www.differencebetween.com/difference-between-syndrome-
and-vs-disease/

even due to multiple disease conditions. Sometimes syndrome is the name given to a set of symptoms before the actual cause is found. One such example is AIDS – acquired immune deficiency syndrome – which referred to the set of symptoms that occur due to HIV infection. The word is still in use even after finding the HIV infection.

Examples for syndromes: Down's syndrome, Parkinson's syndrome, acquired immune deficiency syndrome, cervical syndrome, Cushing's syndrome, restless legs syndrome, scalded skin syndrome, toxic shock syndrome, yellow-nail syndrome, acute radiation syndrome etc.

A **disease** is an abnormality in the normal functioning of the body which is indicated by certain symptoms triggered by a specific cause. Some diseases are grouped into major classes of diseases such as autoimmune diseases. There are many classifications for diseases. In one classification, diseases are divided into 4 main classes as pathogenic diseases, physiological diseases, hereditary diseases, and deficiency diseases. Diseases are also classified as communicable and non-communicable diseases. The characteristic feature of diseases with respect to syndrome is that it has a specific cause, a specific set of symptoms, and consistent change in anatomy.

Examples for diseases: cholera, syphilis, malaria, Lyme disease, meningococcal disease, hepatitis, hemophilia, typhoid fever, meningitis, dengue, measles etc.

What is the difference between syndrome and disease?

- Syndrome is a set of symptoms occurring altogether, but the disease is an abnormality in normal functioning of the body.
- Syndrome does not have a specified cause, but a disease does.
- A syndrome may indicate a disease or even a combination of diseases.
- Two or more different diseases may cause the same syndrome.
- Treating a syndrome is symptomatic but treating a disease allows treating the underlying cause because it is known.

The word dementia

According to Jellinger, the word dementia was first used in the current sense by the French psychiatrist Philippe Pinel, who attempted to describe the different types of psychological behaviours he observed in his patients when working in a psychiatric institution in the late eighteenth and early nineteenth centuries. Pinel differentiated four psychological behaviours, dementia being the fourth. He described dementia as 'the abolition of thinking' whose characteristics were 'no judgment value and the ideas are spontaneous with no connection'. He went on to say:[23]

> The specific character of dementia contains a rapid progression or continual succession of isolated ideas,

---

[23] https://en.wikipedia.org/wiki/Philippe_Pinel

> forgetfulness of previous condition, repetitive acts of exaggeration, decreased responsiveness to external influence and complete lack of judgement.

As a non-medical observer, I am not convinced that this definition describes the behaviours that are associated with our contemporary use of the word dementia in the twenty-first century. I am not sure that the residents I visit in the care home, and who are diagnosed with symptoms of dementia, can be said to have 'abolished thinking', nor to have 'no judgement value'; though, yes, ideas can be spontaneous with no **apparent** connections. Not apparent to us, perhaps, but in their minds there are connections that we cannot grasp.

I would argue that we need to depart from this stark, one-dimensional definition of dementia of Pinel's. From my understanding, Pinel was describing outward behaviours with, as it was understood at the time, psychological causations. The medical and scientific world now knows that the structure of the brain causes the mind to function in particular ways. We now identify many physical events in the brain that cause the mind to alter its capacities in such a way that our behaviours change from the 'normal'.

What does the word dementia mean to us now, in the twenty-first century?

Dementia is a label, a one-word label, that is used to describe a number of conditions with common symptoms, including: confused memory; difficulty with absorbing and processing new information; visual and geographical confusion – not recognising familiar faces and environments leading to disorientation; inability to rationalise an argument.

Some of the diseases that present these symptoms are: Alzheimer's, vascular damage, Lewy body, corticobasal degeneration (CBD, loss of nerve cells), progressive supranuclear palsy (a brain disorder affecting movement and other functions such as swallowing), HIV infection, Niemann-Pick disease type C (harmful accumulation of fatty substances in many organs including the brain), Creutzfeldt-Jakob disease (CJD), Parkinson's disease, Huntington's disease, Down syndrome.

These diseases are misleadingly labelled as dementia. An internet search for the word dementia reveals a mind-boggling minefield of information. Where to start? Depending on which link one clicks, the information will often be contradictory on the number of types of dementia there are, though they all seem to agree on describing the symptoms of dementia.

Here are some examples.

4 types	http://www.dementiauk.org
7+ types	http://www.dementiacare.org.uk
10 types	http://www.healthline.com
12+ types	https://dementiaaustralia.com
13 types	http://www.verywellhealth.com

The Alzheimer's Society UK, quoted in the programme for the play *Still Alice* (staged at the Cambridge Arts Theatre in October 2018), said that 'there are over 100 different types' of dementia.

Here are the types of dementia listed by three influential sites:

10 + types	7+ types	12+ types
healthline.com	dementiacare.org.uk	dementiaaustralia.com

Alzheimer's	Alzheimer's	Alzheimer's disease
Vascular dementia	Vascular dementia	Frontotemporal disorder
Lewy body dementia	Mixed dementia	Lewy bodies
Parkinson's	Lewy body dementia	Vascular damage
Frontotemporal	Frontotemporal dementia	Traumatic brain injury
Creutzfeldt-Jakob		Substance/medication-induced
Wernicke-Korsakoff	Alcohol-related dementia	HIV infection
Mixed dementia	Others	Prion disease
Normal pressure-hydrocephalus		Parkinson's disease
Huntington's disease		Huntington's disease
Other causes		Multiple etiologies
		Unspecified disorder

But we have established that dementia is a syndrome, not a disease. It is a catch-all word that encompasses many diseases. Therefore, there cannot be many dementias. Why then do influential organisations and people persist in deceiving us? For example, writing in *The Times* (London) on 28 January 2020 Dr Mark Porter (who writes a regular health column) said that 'there are a number of types of dementia and they can cause different symptoms'.

There is no such medical category as 'types of dementia'. It is lazy and misleading information at best, misinformation at worst, with catastrophic societal consequences. Apparently, we also die of dementia. The Office for National Statistics (ONS) named 'dementia and Alzheimer's disease' as the leading cause of all deaths – 12.7% – in the UK in 2018.[24] But if dementia is a syndrome and not a disease, how can one die from it?

In general, common symptomatic presentations for all the diseases in the table above are disorientation of time and space, the inability to make links between events (abstract and physical) and poor, or lack of, rationalisation of thought processes.

However, different parts of the brain are damaged by each of these diseases implicated in dementia. So, what are their discrete characteristics? How do they 'contribute to dementia'? Do science and medicine have the answers? Let us look at some examples.

Lewy bodies in the brain were identified by Fritz Heinrich Lewy in 1910 in Berlin. He noticed that some unusual proteins in the brain make people 'act and think differently'. But to this day researchers do not have a full understanding of why Lewy bodies appear or exactly how they contribute to dementia. Knowledge is increasing all the time.

Only recently, a study carried out at the University of Cambridge (and reported in *The Times* on 30 October 2021) revealed that Alzheimer's appears in different parts of the brain at the same time, thus damaging many interconnecting regions of the brain. It is not a disease that progresses from one part of the brain to another as previously thought.

---

[24] https://www.ons.gov.uk Leading causes of death, UK: 2001 to 2018. Published 27 March 2020.

What do professional and governmental organisations say about dementia?

Let us look at definitions by the WHO, the British Psychological Society (BPS), the American Psychological Association (APA) and the National Health Service (NHS) in the UK.

The WHO defines dementia as an acquired syndrome, not a disease, which presents with decline in two or more cognitive functions such as memory and language impairment and inability to make social judgements:

WHO (ICD-11 version 04/2019)

Dementia is an acquired brain syndrome characterized by a decline from a previous level of cognitive functioning with impairment in two or more cognitive domains (such as memory, executive functions, attention, language, social cognition and judgment, psychomotor speed, visuoperceptual or visuospatial abilities). The cognitive impairment is not entirely attributable to normal aging and significantly interferes with independence in the person's performance of activities of daily living ... Based on available evidence, the cognitive impairment is attributed or assumed to be attributable to a neurological or medical condition that affects the brain, trauma, nutritional deficiency, chronic use of specific substances or medications, or exposure to heavy metals or other toxins.

The WHO lists more than fifty (53+) conditions that lead to this collective syndrome with six parent categories of disorders (see Appendix 1):

1. Mental, behavioural or neurodevelopmental disorders.
2. Diseases of the nervous system.
3. Infectious or parasitic diseases.
4. Endocrine, nutritional or metabolic diseases.
5. Traditional medicine conditions.
6. Developmental anomalies.

The BPS defines dementia as:

> a global deterioration of intellectual function due to
> the progressive atrophy of the central nervous system.
> Dementia usually affects those aged 65 and over,
> and presents with a cluster of symptoms, including
> memory loss, confusion, and the potential for sudden
> changes in personality and mood (amongst others).[25]

The fifth edition of the Diagnostic and Statistical Manual (**DSM-5) published by the APA** distinguishes between mild symptoms that do not interfere with normal functioning of everyday life, such as some or momentary difficulties in finding appropriate words to explain an event or some confusion in recognising a person or recalling a name to go with the face. These suggest a mild neurocognitive disorder. If these cognitive processes impede everyday life to such a degree that independent living becomes an impossibility, they are defined as presenting a major neurocognitive disorder. Both degrees of severity may be due to any one of 13 conditions caused by deterioration in the brain's physical structure. Any one of these conditions may present with or without behavioural disturbance:

---

[25] https://www.bps.org.uk/public/a-z-of-psychology#D

- Alzheimer's disease
- frontotemporal lobar degeneration
- Lewy body disease
- vascular disease
- traumatic brain injury
- substance/medication use
- HIV infection
- prion disease
- Parkinson's disease
- Huntington's disease
- another medical condition
- multiple etiologies
- unspecified.

The NHS in England gives the following definition:

> Dementia is a syndrome (a group of related symptoms) associated with an ongoing decline of brain functioning. This may include problems with: memory loss, thinking speed, mental sharpness and quickness, language, understanding, judgement, mood, movement, difficulties carrying out daily activities. There are many different causes of dementia. People often get confused about the difference between Alzheimer's disease and dementia.

Important question: What do these organisations' definitions have in common?

Answer: They are still using the word dementia. Though they are finding causes for these common symptoms, they continue to say that 'dementia is due to ...'

The APA's DSM-5 tells psychiatric doctors that in their diagnosis they must specify whether the disorders, whether mild or major, are 'due to …'

The WHO's ICD-11 suggests a hierarchical approach to diagnosis, which I find disturbing because it labels dementia before finding the physical causes in the brain. For example, Disease 6D80 is listed as being *due to* Alzheimer's as follows:

▸   06 Mental, behavioural or neurodevelopmental disorders
  •   Neurocognitive disorders
  •   Dementia
    »   6D80 Dementia due to Alzheimer disease
▸   Dementia

In Appendix 1 I have constructed a table from the information in WHO ICD-11 that shows how the symptoms are labelled first, **before** diagnosis of a disease that could be triggering the symptoms. This implies that a person is diagnosed with – and therefore labelled as suffering from – dementia when first presenting with the symptoms and that these are deemed as characteristics of dementia. In other words, it suggests that a person is deemed 'mad' **before** anything else.

Here is another example from ICD-11: **6D81 Dementia due to cerebrovascular disease**

▸   06 Mental, behavioural or neurodevelopmental disorders
  •   Neurocognitive disorders
  •   Dementia
    »   6D81 Dementia due to cerebrovascular disease
▸   Dementia

Although the WHO is saying that the symptoms are **due** to dementia (that is, caused by a neurological disease), it is still calling the symptoms dementia – madness.

This does not remove stigma. Neither does the APA's DSM-5, as far as I can deduce, suggest that removing stigma was a consideration when it reclassified these neurological symptoms into mild and major cognitive disorders. Indeed, it seems to reinforce the use of the term dementia as an alternative to the medical and psychological conditions. This seems to be taken up and accepted by organisations involved in research and charitable work such as Dementia Australia,[26] which says on its website, in the document 'Diagnostic Criteria for dementia' (my emphasis):

> Dementia was named major neurocognitive disorder (NCD) in the DSM-5. However, the term dementia **may still** be used as an acceptable alternative. The two terms are essentially different labels for the same condition; major NCD is equivalent to dementia.

The word 'dementia' has become entrenched

There are some additional elements that exacerbate the entrenchment of the word dementia that I believe are of grave concern.

*ONE – **resistance** to change*

Some people living with Alzheimer's and other types of dementia are resistant to any suggestions of change, unless

---

[26] www.dementia.org.au

change is instigated by themselves, because **only they** fully understand the conditions and **only they** can say how they wish to be treated. For instance, Keith Oliver, writing in Kitwood and Brooker's 2019 book *Dementia Reconsidered, Revisited*, was critical of Kitwood's suggestion that role playing is an appropriate strategy for carers to imagine what it must be like to live with a dementia-type cognitive impairment. Oliver says that it is not possible for others to begin to imagine this type of mental turmoil. I wonder what Glenda Jackson (playing the part of Elisabeth in *Elisabeth is Missing*) would think of this suggestion that she may not have given a performance good enough to give us, the audience, a sense of what it must be like to encounter so much resistance on the part of those well-intentioned people in her life who dismissed her as not worthy of listening to? And what about Julianne Moore's performance in the film *Still Alice?*

*TWO – **fear** of losing one's mind*

On Sunday 9 March 2020 a Facebook post by the Alzheimer's Society claimed that one person develops dementia every three minutes and, therefore, we should join the Society's fight by taking part in a 'memory walk' on Sunday 20 March 2020. Is this ethical? What is the point of frightening people into donating to the Alzheimer's Society and equivalent bodies? What is the point of making people feel guilty? This post went on to say that 'dementia is the UK's biggest killer' and, therefore, 'it's time we all knew the truth about dementia'. I could not agree more. But which truth? That dementia kills or that it does not kill? That dementia is a disease or that it is not a disease? We have established that dementia is a syndrome and not a disease. Should public bodies not begin to tell people this truth?

*THREE – press **sensationalism** about the causes of dementia*

Here are three examples of sensationalist headlines that distract from the truth about dementia.

▸ Incidences of dementia are associated with cardiovascular health at age 50 (*British Medical Journal*, August 2019)
▸ Abnormal blood pressure in middle age and late life influences dementia risk (*Science News* – John Hopkins Medicine, August 2019)
▸ Chief executives have lower dementia risk than farmers (*The Times*, 19 August 2021). This suggests that mentally stimulating jobs stave off dementia – how insulting is this to those of us in less lofty positions?

Figures published by the ONS on 27 March 2020 declared 'dementia and Alzheimer's' together as the leading cause (12.7%) of all deaths registered in the UK between 2011 and 2018. It was the leading cause of death in women in 2018 at 16.5%. The ONS speculates, in the same article, that this may be due to a number of reasons, including 'increased reporting of dementia on death certificates':

> There are several reasons why the number of deaths from dementia and Alzheimer disease has increased in recent years. Dementia and Alzheimer disease are more likely to occur among older age groups, and more people are living longer and surviving other illnesses. In addition, a better understanding of dementia and improved diagnosis is likely to have caused increased reporting of dementia on death certificates. This may be a consequence of initiatives put in place in 2013 to 2014, such as the Prime Minister's challenge on

dementia and the government's mandate to NHS
England, which included an ambition that two-thirds
of the estimated number of people with dementia in
England should have a diagnosis.

There was a 2011 update to the coding framework
and a 2014 update to the coding framework used to
code cause of death. These updates increased the
number of deaths coded with an underlying cause of
dementia.

An important question that ensues from this: why are doctors
putting dementia on death certificates as a cause of death
more often than they used to? A thorough investigation would
be necessary to identify the underlying reasons, beyond the
scope of this manifesto. I am inclined to speculate that this
increased reporting of dementia as a cause of death on death
certificates might be due to governmental pressure to diagnose
dementia in order to galvanise medical research. The UK set
itself up as the country leading the world on tackling dementia
via the Prime Minister's Challenge on Dementia in 2010, but
I hope that dementia has not become yet another political
football.

*What do WE – you and me, the general public – understand
when we hear that someone we know has dementia?*

The current medical definition[27] of dementia suggests that,
while it affects the **ability** to perform in rational ways, it does

---

[27] http://www.medical-dictionary.thefreedictionary.com/Dementia
'Dementia is a loss of mental ability severe enough to interfere with normal
activities of daily living, lasts more than six months, not present since birth,
and not associated with a loss or alteration of consciousness'.

not take away the sense of awareness and consciousness. In other words, when we are affected by this condition, we are no longer able to think and behave as we did before its onset, because our brain's **ability** to string words and events together in a chronological and logical manner will have been impaired. When ability is impaired, it becomes a disability. Disability is not madness. It is not 'raving'.[28]

This label 'dementia' has done untold damage, psychologically and culturally, over a number of generations. It has disempowered families, friends and professionals of the skills to adapt, linguistically and emotionally. More importantly, dementia is the most insulting of terms. When we say to someone, in anger, 'you are totally demented' or 'you are completely out of your mind', we are insulting that person's state of being and integrity.

People living with this condition still have the form of, what I call, mental agility for the mind gymnastics that take place in the brain in the space of nanoseconds: the multitasking our brains are capable of. For example, in my 'normal' brain this sequence could be thinking what treats should I take to my grandchildren next week while I am writing this down and at the same time remembering to check the time on my mobile because the library will close at 13.00 today and do I need to stop at the supermarket for some food or do I have enough in the fridge for the next two days because I probably won't feel like going out tomorrow ... and so on.

---

[28] https://www.etymonline.com/search?q=dementia

When I observed my mother's seemingly meaningless mental sequencing – that is, meaningless to 'normal' listeners and observers – the thinking events that I was witnessing would present themselves as if out of time and wrongly placed with no reference to that particular moment in time: the smell of coffee would take her to a visit she had shared with a cousin in Italy many years ago, which she was reliving as if it were happening now, in her sitting room in England. Just because I found it hard to make sense of what she was saying did not mean that she did not know what she was talking about. It was up to me to work out how to get her to explain to me what she was referring to in a way that I could understand.

By adjusting the way I used language with my mother I became aware that she remained the same feisty woman, the same determined controller, the same sensitive mother that I had always known. In her new condition her mental gymnastics took her from happy events in Italy to happy events in England as if they were one and the same event, from anger and frustration at her helplessness in making ends meet as a home manager in her new home in England to anger and frustration at her helplessness in not being able to give her children all that she would have liked to have given when she was a young mother in Italy. My mother was still the same person. Her mental gymnastics had morphed into time events that knew no space boundaries. A fusion of time and space was taking place in her mind. It was fascinating to watch this happen in front of my eyes. It was as if her life had been lived and was being lived in a continuous dimension of time in one limitless space.

An alternative to the dementia label

Thus, I developed my theories that people diagnosed with symptoms associated with dementia are not mad, they do not disappear into a psychological vacuum and instead they present an intriguing picture of time and space. I did not know how to imagine this until I read Carlo Rovelli's definition of the 'extended present'.[29]

As I began to read and my knowledge increased about this phenomenon labelled as dementia, I became aware that my ideas are not new nor revolutionary. If an idea is plausible it is quite likely that other people have considered it. And indeed that is the case.

On the need to alter language:

> There undoubtedly remains a way to go in removing what is viewed as the unacceptable and stigmatizing language around dementia.[30]

On the concept of being the same person:

> Human beings with dementia are persons, in both fundamentally the same way and yet, at the same time, in different ways than they were before.[31]

---

[29] Carlo Rovelli (2018). *The Order of Time*. Penguin Random House UK.
[30] Clair Surr, critiquing chapter 9 in Kitwood, Brooker (ed.) 2019. *Dementia Reconsidered, Revisited*, p 172.
[31] Jan Dewing, critiquing chapter 1 in Kitwood, Brooker (ed.) 2019. *Dementia Reconsidered, Revisited*, p 22.

On the concept of time and space dimensions:

> People with dementia can travel across this
> domain (of negative experience) many times and in
> different directions ... The journey is, to some extent,
> independent of the ordinary sense of the linear course
> of time.[32]

So, let us start by replacing the term dementia (madness) with
Amelesia (unmindfulness).

Amelesia is the condition or state of unmindfulness. It is a
compound noun made from Ameles, which in Greek means
unmindfulness, and the Greek suffix –sia, which means the
state or the condition in which one is found to be, psychologically
and/or physically.

Can Amelesia replace the word dementia when describing
the condition that affects millions of people worldwide who
display symptoms of damaged memory capacities, poor mental
coordination, disorientation, inability to reason and other
symptoms associated with such diseases as Alzheimer's and
Lewy bodies?

These diseases have been conveniently grouped under the
term dementia. But we have seen that dementia is not a
disease. The word dementia describes a psychological state
brought about by damage to the neural and cellular networks
in the physical structure of the brain. The damage caused by

---

[32] Tom Kitwood, chapter 5 in Kitwood, Brooker (ed.) 2019. *Dementia
Reconsidered, Revisited*, p 91.

these events prevents information from travelling around the brain in the usual way, because parts of these circuits are blocked by the damage. The term dementia has become an all-encompassing word to describe the symptoms that present as a result of this damage, but they are caused by lots of different and unique events.

We have established that people affected by these types of damage to their brains are not mad as suggested by the word dementia. I have suggested that they have entered a state of unmindfulness, because they appear unable of using their mental capabilities in a mindful way, as I understand it. That is, the damaged brain is not able to focus on mental and physical events in the same way as the non-damaged brain can. It follows, therefore, that if people living with Alzheimer's and similar conditions cannot be 'mindful', they must be 'unmindful'. To be more confident, we will take a brief look at mindfulness in the section on intent 3 later on when we consider the concepts of time and space.

Stop saying that the person that we knew 'has gone' – recognise the permanence of the core inner person

It is my strong contention that a person living with a condition such as Alzheimer's does not disappear in some mental vacuum that defies description. It is heart-rending and insulting beyond human understanding that a life – which is what to me 'a person' is – can be dismissed in such cruel terms. And yet, that is what the medical and caring professions tell us happens to a person diagnosed with mental decline. It is devastating for their families and friends. It is immoral towards the people in receipt of this prognosis.

This attitude persists among the medical profession and it works its way through all levels and dimensions of social and medical care provided in the community and in residential care homes. It persists in spite of the incredible work that has been carried out over the last twenty years or so by people such as Tom Kitwood,[33] whose Dementia Care Mapping (DCM) revolutionised care. But, sadly, the general attitudes that he strove to eradicate towards people diagnosed with Alzheimer's persist. His book was revised early in 2019 with commentaries on each chapter by a number of academics, edited by Dawn Brooker. There is a strong consensus expressed in the revised book that much work needs to be done to reinforce Kitwood's massive contribution to the field of dementia care and to take it further by adding current thinking.[34]

Kitwood's DCM manual underpins much of the training for senior managers in the dementia care field. But how much of that is incorporated in the early stages of training for basic level care? Kitwood identified a 'malignant social psychology' towards dementia (Brooker 2019, p 3), which he placed as the responsibility of individuals in their relationships with people living with dementia. In her critique of this individual responsibility (expressed in chapter 1 of Brooker's revisiting of Kitwood's book) Jan Dewing considers the responsibility of a community whose culture must change fundamentally towards people living with Alzheimer's and similar conditions. Care, she says, must 'take place within the overall culture' and 'not just in terms of its being a relationship between individuals'. This is fundamental. But how does one change a societal cultural attitude?

Individual families need to be told a different story by the medical professions, by their family doctors and by the psychiatrists who diagnose the mental impairments. It is

---

[33] Tom Kitwood published his influential book *Dementia Reconsidered: The person comes first* in 1997 (Buckingham: Open University Press).

[34] Kitwood, Brooker (ed.) 2019. *Dementia Reconsidered, Revisited.*

individuals who make up a community within which a culture is born and flourishes.

Kitwood identified the idea of 'personhood' as the key to changing dementia care. That is, if we can understand what it is to be a person then we might change the way we see those living with dementia. As a psychologist, Kitwood spent a great deal of time looking at the concept of personhood in psychology and in philosophy.

Kitwood's aim was for the individual carer to understand the varied dimensions of personhood and thus, by instinct, treat the care home resident with dementia differently. I believe that to a great extent this has been achieved. But I agree with the modern academics who critiqued each chapter in his book that much else needs to be done to enhance his work and build on it.

My aim is much simpler. Less academic. More down to earth. Humbler. I want the young carers who have just been given two days' training on basic physical care to feel more confident and at ease chatting with the people they are caring for. It is perfectly feasible to incorporate the ideas presented at the start of this manifesto within a short basic training for this to be effective: the person does not die (metaphorically speaking); it is possible to have meaningful conversations if we stop thinking of time and space in 'normal' terms.

And so, what, you will ask, do I mean by 'the person'? Probably exactly the same as you, reading this, understand by the word person. I accept the medical and scientific evidence that the physical brain, affected by damage brought about by such diseases, causes the mind to behave in unexpected, and maybe hitherto unfamiliar, ways. I do not accept that the totality of a person's being is destroyed. I demonstrated in my memoir about my mother's mental decline caused by mini strokes (known currently as vascular dementia) that her core person – the caring daughter, wife and mother, the person obsessed with her duties as the family carer – never abandoned her.

I have observed this phenomenon as a volunteer visitor in a residential care home when discussing the essential character of a resident with members of their family. Even in extreme advanced stages I watched a daughter and father enjoy listening together to the beautiful operatic arias that they had enjoyed in a previous togetherness. He knew his daughter through their common love of music. Until his death he remained the gently spoken elegant gentleman he had always been.

There is one aspect of the core personality that I observed in my mother and I continually note every time I meet a new resident coming to live in the care home I visit: the indelible power of a strong event in a person's life, an event that is never forgotten and always remembered. My mother never forgot that her eldest son had died after a short life of severe illness and disability. Someone that we will call Mary never forgot joining her father, as a sixteen-year-old, trying to rescue people engulfed by a 'ball of fire' in her street, during the Second World War. At that moment she realised her dad was the most self-less person she would ever know and never stopped looking up to him and admiring his steadfastness. She always said he had been her role model. She described that moment so clearly and vividly as if she were living it.

My idea of a 'core' personality is the one dominant behavioural trait of our character by which other people describe us. For example, a 'domineering father', a 'kind teacher', a 'thoughtful musician', a 'diligent athlete', a 'calm person in an emergency', an 'angry manager', a 'bossy sister', a 'self-absorbed mother', an 'arrogant friend' and so on. We describe people we know well and those we have just met with very simple adjectives that tell us exactly what we know of a specific behaviour. We have learned to do this via our life experiences encompassing all of our interactions with all sorts of people, from childhood to our present adulthood.

Challengers to this approach will expect substantiation of this concept of a core personality in psychological and/or neurological terms, drawn from scientific evidence. However, I am writing this for the daughter, for the sister, for the husband, for the friend of all those people living with this kind of decline in mental agility. They are not interested in learning about the different types of personalities identified by the myriad of personality tests. Nor how philosophers have defined personality over the ages, nor the academic arguments about what a person is.

When I ask a young carer in the care home that I visit what a new resident is like, I do not get descriptions such as 'he's an alpha male' or 'she is neurotic' or 'he's an introvert', the sorts of personality definitions found in the literature. I am told that Peter, who came to live in the residential care home two weeks ago, is a bit flirty, with twinkling eyes, or that Sylvia is very softly spoken and very polite.

It is in these simple terms that **communicative interactions** need to take place between the still mentally agile people and those with declining mental and verbal skills, because:

> Human beings with dementia are persons, in both
> fundamentally the same way and yet, at the same
> time, in different ways than they were before.[35]

There seems to be more agreement now, in the first quarter of the twenty-first century, among psychologists and neuroscientists, that the mind is a product of the neurology of the physical structures in the brain.[36] There is also agreement that our life experiences shape the development of the thinking that our brain produces. In these terms my concept of a 'core' person is the essential personality that emerges as a combination of learned behaviours and genetic tendencies. I am the product of an Italo–English cultural pastiche. I am also the daughter of two distinct individuals who had certain attitudes to life and ways of seeing the world, which present themselves in my behaviours and in my thinking. I can amend them and modify them with respect to the contexts of my life, but they are recognisably their genetic propensities that they have passed on to me.

I particularly like Carlo Rovelli's own beautiful concept[37] of who and what we really are, in our very essence:

> We are histories of ourselves. Narratives. I am not
> this momentary mass of flesh reclined on the sofa,
> typing the letter 'a' on my laptop; I am my thoughts
> full of the traces of the phrases that I am writing; I am

---

[35] Jan Dewing, critiquing chapter 1 in Kitwood, Brooker (ed.) 2019. *Dementia Reconsidered, Revisited*, p 22.
[36] Mariano Sigman (2017). *The Secret Life of the Mind. How our brain thinks, feels and decides*. William Collins.
[37] Rovelli (2018). *The Order of Time*, p 154.

my mother's caresses, and the serene kindness with which my father calmly guided me; I am my adolescent travels; I am what my reading has deposited in layers in my mind; I am my loves, my moments of despair, my friendships, what I have written, what I have heard; the faces engraved on my memory. I am, above all, the one who a minute ago made a cup of tea for himself. The one who a moment ago typed the word 'memory' into his computer. The one who just composed the sentence that I am now completing. If all this disappeared, would I still exist? I am this long, ongoing novel. My life consists of it.

Rethink the concept of time and space in the disabled mind – a continuous present

When I am in conversation with an Amelesian I have the feeling that time is suspended. In fact, time ceases to have any relevance. The words that we are using and the thoughts we are exchanging are the only important elements of our encounter. They alone give meaning to our chat at that moment. We move from one 'time zone' to another with ease and no forethought. And it feels comfortable and natural.

Take the short exchange on the next page with Pam,[38] who is bedbound and cannot feed herself. She is often heard calling out to her mother.

---

[38] Pam lives in Redbond Lodge care home. Her family gave me permission to use her real name in the book of conversations *Come and Talk With Me* that I published in 2021. The above extract is from a longer conversation in that book.

Mina: Good morning, Pam, how are you today?

Pam: I am alright. I am always alright! Can I have some
           breakfast?

Mina: Yes of course. What would you like?

Pam: What is there?

Mina: There's porridge. You sometimes have porridge.
           (Pam always has porridge)

Pam: Do I?

Mina: Hmmm.

Pam: Okay. I'll have some porridge.

*I leave the room to go and get the breakfast. I hear Pam as I
move down the corridor.*

Pam: Mum, come and get me. Mum, come and get me.
           Mum, come and get me.

Mina: There we are, Pam. I have your porridge ... and cup
           of tea.

Pam: That's nice. I love a cup of tea.

Mina: It's all a bit too hot still. We'll let it all cool down for
           a minute, Pam. Is that alright?

Pam: Yeah, that's alright.

Mina: Is your mother coming today, Pam?

Pam: My mother? No, I don't think so. No, she can't,
           can she?

Mina: Why not?

Pam: Because she's dead, isn't she?

Mina: Ah ... how long has she been dead?

Pam: A long time.

Pam seems to live her mental life in what Carlo Rovelli calls
'the extended present':

> Between the past and the future of an event (for
> example, between the past and the future for you,

where you are, and in the precise moment in which
you are reading) there exists an 'intermediate zone',
an 'expanded present.'[39]

I observed the same phenomenon in my mother's mind, and
in the way it expressed itself:

The past and the present became one … Time and
space were unified in the reality of remembered
episodes, bursts of memories that presented
themselves to her mind in cinematic snapshots.'[40]

At any one moment – by which I mean a moment as known and
understood by the non-disabled brain – the mind disabled by
this syndrome called dementia, or rather the Amelesian mind,
may not be able to demonstrate that it can stop, focus and pay
attention to a mental task for longer than a few nanoseconds,
if that.

When I ask Pam if she would like a sip of her tea, she replies
yes while her mind is in a different time and space zone. In her
brain, it seems to me, time and space have no demarcations, in
the way the healthy brain places experiences in chronological
order. It seems to me that her brain is not able to focus on 'this
moment' on 'this now'. She is not being mindful, because her
mind is covering the whole spectrum of her life's experience.

This is why I propose that the word Amelesia reflects much
more accurately this mind that wanders through time and

[39] Carlo Rovelli (2014). *Reality Is Not What It Seems: The journey to
quantum gravity*. Penguin Random House UK, p 53.
[40] From my 2017 memoir *Thank You Lady*, p 15.

space unencumbered by details such as 'before' and 'after', dates and names of places. This mind is not mad.

So, what does it mean to be mindful?

Modern approaches to mindfulness are many and very varied, but each derives its philosophy and approach from the traditional Buddhist tenet that **to be mindful is to focus one's attention to what is happening now, in the present moment.** To be mindful in this sense, means a) to distinguish between what is good for one's wellbeing – at a particular moment in time – and what is not good; and b) to be able to calm the mind once this distinction has been made.

Mindfulness is now almost ubiquitous. It has been adopted by many psychologists and educationalists as a tool for the development of focused attention of body and mind. It is considered an effective skill useful in all aspects of life, from keeping anxiety at a healthy level in order to function positively in everyday life, to preparing for examinations and other tests. At the time of writing (2021), mindfulness is used for many theories and practices, including these five examples.

1. *Present moment awareness*: to give one's complete attention to *this moment's* experience.[41]
2. *Present-centred awareness*: feelings and thoughts that come to our attention at any particular moment in our mind that are accepted and not questioned.[42]

---

[41] DS Black (2011). A brief definition of mindfulness. Mindfulness Research Guide. http://www.mindfulexperience.org
[42] Scott R Bishop et al. (2004). Mindfulness: a proposed operational definition. *Clinical Psychology: Science and Practice* 11(3): 230–241.

3. *Informal mindfulness*: using mindfulness in everyday life.[43]
4. *Self-regulation of attention and orientation of experience in the present moment*: to be aware of current experiences (*self-regulation*) and to be curious about what is exactly happening (*orientation*).[44]
5. *Interaction* between *attention* and *peripheral awareness*: two discrete states in which we may be aware of things around us; there is a distinction between paying attention to something and being aware of something.[45]

In the early stages of Amelesia there are elements of all the above. The communicative approach to conversations (see intent 4) that I have developed and successfully piloted[46] suggests that with appropriate communication techniques it is possible to guide Amelesians to focus their attention on the here and now, as in present moment awareness (theory 1 above), no matter how brief the moment might be. This attention is temporary and fleeting.

I suggest that the second of the above theories – present-centred awareness – is very much a feature of Amelesia. None of the Amelesians that I have encountered question their thoughts. In fact, they are so convinced of their veracity and power that they get very agitated if contradicted.

---

[43] SF Hicks (2009). *Mindfulness and Social Work*. Lyceum, Chicago.

[44] Bishop et al. (2004). Mindfulness: a proposed operational definition.

[45] John Yates, Matthew Immergut, Jeremy Graves (2017). *The Mind Illuminated: A complete meditation guide integrating Buddhist wisdom and brain science for greater mindfulness*. Dharma Treasure Press.

[46] https://www.amelesia.com

Amelesians are not able to use mindfulness in everyday life (theory 3), nor can they make any connections between what they are experiencing (theory 4) with what is happening around them (theory 5).

People affected by symptoms associated with diseases such as Alzheimer's – disorientation, confusion, fear, anxiety, anger – do not have the mental ability or agility to be present in the moment. If they manage it, it is a fleeting sense of being part of an event such as drinking a cup of tea or acknowledging a greeting (Good morning!). They are not able to process what is happening 'now' and add it to the sum of their life's experiences.

This raises the question: what is a moment? Those affected by Alzheimer's-like symptoms are also living in the moment, but their 'moment' could be any moment of their previous life, which is as present in their mind as if it were happening now – meaning 'now' as understood by those of us who are not, or believe that we are not, living with Alzheimer's-like symptoms. Instead, they are living in a continuous present, as described by Carlo Rovelli.

Carlo Rovelli and other scientists are questioning whether the brain mimics time and space in the conventional sense. Rovelli says that it is impossible to define what time is in our universe. So much takes place simultaneously and yet not at the 'same time'. Everything overlaps and intertwines as if a 'blurring' of everything else:

> Temporality is profoundly linked to blurring. The
> blurring is due to the fact that we are ignorant of the
> microscopic details of the world.[47]

Is this how our brain is wired to see our life? As a 'global' vision
of all our experience up to this very moment 'blurred' into one
long film shot? Does our life show itself, in our damaged brain,
as a 'wholeness' that is eternally present (while we live) in our
minds? Do we see distinct 'pieces' highlighted as we scan it,
just as we might scan a panorama with binoculars: different
bits come into focus as we move the binoculars?

Apparently, some physicists have been considering whether
our brains see our life events as a film. The neuroscientist
Dean Buonomano in his book *Your Brain is a Time Machine*
considers this idea. He quotes the physicist Julian Barbour
describing watching a kingfisher in flight:[48]

> My brain contains, at any one instant, several
> 'snapshots' at once. The brain ... somehow 'plays the
> movie' for me ... I see ... six or seven snapshots of the
> kingfisher just as they occurred in the flight I saw. This
> brain configuration, with its simultaneous coding of
> several snapshots, nevertheless belongs to just one ...

Julian Barbour is saying that when our brain sees something
happening with an object or animal or person in it, it makes
immediate links to other times when we observed the same

[47] Rovelli (2018). *The Order of Time*, p 123.
[48] Dean Buonomano (2018). *Your Brain is a Time Machine: The
neuroscience and physics of time.* W W Norton and Company, p 171.

object/animal/person and multiple images present themselves to our mind at the same instant.

Mindfulness training

Could Amelesians benefit from mindfulness training?

The *moment-to-moment* theory of mindfulness seems to be key in current thinking: 'mindfulness means knowing directly what is going on inside and outside of ourselves, moment by moment'.[49] At low levels of brain damage, Amelesians know what is going on in their mind. They just know it in a different way. Their moment by moment is in the past, not in the here and now as we understand it. We should perhaps say that they are not in the 'present moment'. The NHS website quotes Professor Mark Williams, former director of the Oxford Mindfulness Centre:

> This [mindfulness] lets us stand back from our thoughts and start to see their patterns. Gradually, we train ourselves to notice when our thoughts are taking over and realise that thoughts are simply 'mental events' that do not have to control us.

And this is the point: thoughts control the mental and physical life of people with Amelesia. It is as if thoughts become entities that come unbidden and unwanted.

Perhaps the best example of what Amelesians cannot do is this advice on how to practise mindfulness, ironically from the same NHS website:

---

[49] https://nhs.uk/conditions/stress-anxiety-depression/mindfulness

> Free yourself from the past and future ... realise that,
> for several minutes, you have been trapped in reliving
> past problems or pre-living future worries.

That is exactly where Amelesians are: trapped in their past, reliving their past. But they do not realise it. Because their past is their 'now'. Their present lies in needing reassurance that the people in their life – husband, daughter, grandson – might visit, take them home, not abandon them ... All the people with this mental decline with whom I have chatted in the care home over the past five years and more are heard saying things like this: 'Mum, come and help me'; 'Mum, where are you?'; 'Mum, when are you coming?' They are calling their dead mother (the past) to come and be with them now (the present), not sometime (the future).

So, what can we do? While waiting for this change to happen, the **communicative training programme** I present places the onus on us, the 'normally functioning' people, to learn to interact with the Amelesians in our lives so that they can be, for a moment, in the moment with us.[50]

---

[50] A Communicative Approach: The Amelesia Training Programme. Available on https://amelesia.com

Learn how to sustain meaningful conversations with Amelesians

The communicative approach to conversations

What is it and what difference would it make to interactions between Amelesians and non-Amelesians?

The reconceptualisation of dementia will be achieved by training people to adopt a *communicative approach* to conversations with people whose mental capabilities have been impaired by conditions such as Alzheimer's.

We, all of us in society, must learn to communicate in a meaningful way with others diagnosed with Alzheimer's or similar conditions. These conditions have no class or educational barriers. It could be me or you. Any one of us. At any age.

Through good communication we will make three discoveries:

▸ the person diagnosed with this condition is still there, in the altered mind
▸ the altered mind is not mad
▸ time and space are experienced differently by the mind altered by physical changes in the brain as a result of these conditions.

I write this for the daughters and sons, for the mothers and fathers, for the sisters and brothers, for the carers and nurses – and other professionals – who are, or will be, interacting with people diagnosed with Alzheimer's or similar conditions. The behavioural symptoms associated with these conditions are, in general, impaired memory, confusion and a decreasing ability to lead an independent life as a consequence of these disabilities. Slowly those affected become totally reliant on the people around them for every need.

The most challenging of these needs is communication. Nobody understands them. They do not understand anybody else. A total breakdown in communication occurs. They make no sense to us and we make no sense to them. In these circumstances we dismiss them. They cannot understand why we ignore what they say. We tell ourselves that they are no longer themselves. We think they do not know what they are saying.

But they do. They know what they are saying. We just do not know how to interpret it. Because we do not understand what is happening in their mind. We do not have the key to their jumbled-up thoughts. We conclude that they have changed so much. We do not recognise them. Therefore they must be mad.

But that is not so.

The communicative approach to conversations is rooted in linguistic theories that place learners in simulated real-life situations so that they can practise the language necessary in that situation. Imagining ourselves in real situations and acting out roles we might encounter (for example, buying a railway ticket or arriving at an accident and emergency hospital) sharpens our understanding of the language needed in that context and enables us to practise it until we obtain the desired results.

In a sense, it is somewhat formulaic. We learn certain phrases and vocabulary that are better for creating meaning in that particular situation. When we are at the doctor's we need to have specific words and phrases at our disposal and how to put them in precise questions so that we can say exactly what we need to say. We also learn, in these artificially created real-life situations, how to listen carefully for the information that is coming our way from the other person in order to interpret it correctly as it was intended. When in the company of people whose mind is affected by reduced skills in decoding rapid information, we need to imagine ourselves in that same mental situation and adapt the way we speak so that we can communicate with them without too much anxiety and frustration.

This should be the approach of everyone involved in any type of interaction with people living with impaired brain capabilities, and especially so of professionals, as suggested by a group of academics who carried out a survey of people's opinions of language used in this blurred area of human communication:[51]

> The responsibility to communicate with people living with dementia and their families in language they can understand and relate to is incumbent on the professional, regardless of their discipline.

Because, concluded the authors of this study:

> Words have the power to shape thoughts, beliefs, emotions and behaviour.

If we change the way we communicate with people affected by cognitive impairment, and if we adapt our language to their new way of seeing the world, we will begin to view them in a different way. We will stop seeing them as mad and incapable. We will realise that it is possible to hold good, meaningful conversations with them. By asking the right questions, by listening carefully to what the other person is saying, we pick up cues. We build on those cues. We give prompts and we change words and phrases to make our meanings clearer. We refer to real people and real events. All these interactional strategies are at the centre of the communicative approach to conversations that is at the heart of my training programme.

The communicative approach has a well-established place in theories of language teaching and learning, since it was

---

[51] E Wolverson, H Birtles, E Moniz-Cook, I James, D Brooker, F Duffy (2019). Naming and framing the behavioural and psychological symptoms of dementia (BPSD) paradigm: professional stakeholder perspectives. *OBM Geriatrics* 3(4): 1–19.

developed in the 1970s by the linguists Hymes[52] and Halliday.[53] It is widely used around the world in classes of all ages for additional language learning.

My training programme encompasses key teaching and learning strategies of the communicative approach to conversational interactions: games, problem-solving tasks, role plays, group work, sharing opinions, scaffolding and a linguistic underpinning of question formation. It draws on the real experiences of the people involved in the interactions. Its central tenet is placing learner speakers of a language in a situational context in which appropriate and specific language must be used, as in the example above of visiting the doctor. Participants are asked to imagine themselves as people diagnosed with dementia-like symptoms and as 'normal' visitors, before and after learning the linguistic conversational techniques that lead to sustained dialogue.

---

[52] D Hymes (1971). *On Communicative Competence*. University of Pennsylvania Press, Philadelphia.
[53] MAK Halliday (1975). *Learning How to Mean: Explorations in the development of language*. Edward Arnold, London.

How does the communicative approach fit into existing training programmes?

There must be countless training programmes on how to care for and communicate with people living with Alzheimer's-type symptoms. Every college of further education in England that runs a programme on social care will be using a particular course of study. Undergraduate and postgraduate studies on dementia at numerous universities in the UK have developed their own courses, with specific strands on acquiring communication skills.

There is a big push from the UK government (conceived under the Prime Minister's Challenge on Dementia initiative) for society at large to acquire appropriate skills in order to provide optimal support to people diagnosed and living with Alzheimer's-type conditions. As mentioned in the introduction, the NHS has also produced professional training standards in order to reduce the stigma associated with dementia.

Volunteers and carers, staff in cafes and restaurants, hairdressers and plumbers, students and builders, daughters and mothers – we are all exhorted to acquire these skills, underpinned by the person-centred approach espoused by Kitwood. Twenty-two schools piloted a scheme 'to create a more dementia friendly generation through education' and the Alzheimer's Society established Dementia Friendly Awards in 2014. Businesses of all types (including, controversially, betting shops) have been encouraged to become 'dementia friendly' environments.

Health Education England commissioned a study by Professor Claire Surr of Leeds Becket University to find out 'the types of training programmes which lead to the best outcomes for people with dementia and their families'.[54]

I have looked at various courses in order to become familiar with their purpose and content. I am confident that the communicative approach that I have developed and which has been successfully piloted will make a contribution as an additional module to existing programmes of study. Here are some examples:

▸ The English NHS published guidelines in 2013 (updated January 2022) for all nurses to show competence in the 6Cs: care, compassion, competence, communication, courage, commitment. The *communication* competence requires nurses to self-assess on whether they 'communicate

---

[54] Department of Health (March 2016). *Prime Minister's Challenge on Dementia 2020. Implementation Plan.* p 45.

sensitively to support meaningful interaction' with those they are caring for.

▸ The NHS has published the *Dementia Training Standards Framework*.[55] Standard 5 on communication requires trainees to be able to communicate effectively and compassionately with individuals who 'have dementia'.

▸ NICE published guidelines[56] in 2018 for the assessment, management and support of people living with dementia on how to adapt communication styles to improve interactions with the person living with dementia.

▸ Dementia UK and HEDN (Higher Education for Dementia Network) have developed *A Curriculum for UK Dementia Education*.[57] Put together by a large consortium of academics from several universities, this is a comprehensive framework for essential requirements for a rounded knowledge and skill base for professionals wishing to work in the area of dementia. Communicating well with people with dementia is one of the ten core topics in this curriculum. Its underpinning principles (some are particularly pertinent to my Amelesia communicative approach) are that, as a result of interaction with professionals working with them, people living with dementia:

• are empowered
• enjoy life

---

[55] Skills for Health et al. (2018). Dementia Training Standards Framework. https://www.skillsforhealth.org.uk/services/item/176-dementia-core-skills-education-and-training-framework

[56] NICE (2018). Dementia: assessment, management and support. http://www.nice.org.uk/guidance/ng97

[57] Dementia UK (undated). A Curriculum for UK Dementia Education: Developed by the Higher Education for Dementia Network (HEDN). https://www.dementiauk.org/for-professionals/how-to-become-an-admiral-nurse/download-the-curriculum-for-demenita-education

- experience emotional wellbeing at all times
- have good relationships
- are understood.

▸ Another training programme by Skills for Health, which is online and freely available to all, is Stand By Me.[58] Drawing from Kitwood's person-centred approach this course includes a section on good communication in order to prevent feelings of anxiety and agitation in people living with dementia. It does not suggest any types of appropriate question in order to engage in and sustain meaningful dialogue. The Amelesia approach as an additional module would provide this missing and essential component.

▸ Companies who own and/or manage residential care homes and who design their own training in care provision might be interested in enhancing the training they provide for the staff they recruit with my communicative approach. For example, Runwood Homes (the parent company of Redbond Lodge residential care home in Great Dunmow, which I visit and where I piloted the communicative approach) provides a comprehensive training programme, which culminates in the Care Certificate. The programme deals with communication in a broad sense, within the spectrum of 'communication at work' (standard 6) and within the context of conflict resolution (standard 3 'duty of care') should misunderstanding arise with family members of a resident. The Amelesia communicative approach would enhance such training to equip carers with stronger linguistic tools so that they learn to communicate more effectively with residents.

---

[58] https://www.skillsplatform.org/courses/2310-stand-by-me-dementia1

▶ Many charitable organisations have produced dementia resources for school pupils. The Amelesia communicative approach could complement existing programmes. For instance, the Alzheimer's Society produced *A Dementia Resource Suite for Schools*, which teachers can adapt to various age groups and insert within their personal, spiritual and health education programmes. The sixth form students who piloted my Amelesia training volunteered to participate as part of their school's community service programme.

The training programme

My course **A Communicative Approach: The Amelesia Training Programme** was successfully piloted with a small group of sixth form students from Felsted School in Felsted, Great Dunmow, Essex. The pilot study is published in full on my website at https://amelesia.com. The programme encompassed face-to-face training on the communicative approach to conversations, visits to residents living in Redbond Lodge care home in Great Dunmow, and written and verbal reflections on the benefits of the communicative approach for sustained dialogue between visitors and residents.

Evaluations of this pilot suggest applicability across the board. For example, it would be useful in:

▶ schools and colleges for 16–19-year-olds
▶ society at large, such as for community visitors and artists working with people living with Alzheimer's and similar diseases
▶ the caring professions: my scrutiny of training programmes for the caring professions suggests that this communicative approach can be incorporated into existing training

programmes for carers and other professionals, such as the Admiral Nurses set up by Dementia UK

▸ university programmes on dementia: again, this communicative approach could easily be incorporated into existing modules.

My communicative approach training programme can also stand on its own. It is well suited to students in colleges of further education studying to become carers and to sixth form students who wish to answer this call to alter society's concept of dementia. It can work as a short CPD (continuous professional development) course for in-service carers, to remind them periodically of how they can sustain more meaningful conversations with those in their care.

Conclusions

Food for thought and the way ahead

We have seen that many people and organisations have been working hard for a very long time to change attitudes towards a condition that is affecting millions of people worldwide. A condition that is frightening and bewildering. We have seen that governments all over the world are engaged at national levels and cooperating internationally through charitable bodies, the OECD and the WHO (among others) to find ways to 'improve the lives of people with dementia'.[59]

The UK government set up a loneliness programme with a Minister for Loneliness in charge. Improving the lives of people living with Alzheimer's and similar conditions is one aspect being considered, as suggested by the presence of Alzheimer's Society UK among members of its network tasked with implementing the loneliness policy. Included in the network's remit is the inclusion of young people in breaking down the societal barriers that lead to loneliness.

---

[59] *Prime Minister's Challenge on Dementia 2020* (2015), p 63.

The communicative approach presented in this manifesto is perfect for young people who wish to do away with intergenerational differences and see all members of society as contributing to harmonious living.

Young people are the catalyst for change. The students who participated in the pilot study were struck by how much their view of people living with cognitive impairment changed during the course of their visits to residents in Redbond Lodge.

For all of us, attitudes will not change fundamentally until we stop calling this decline dementia, nor while we continue to see people with this condition as no longer valuable or useful in their own right.

Dementia has become a familiar topic of discussion on the radio and as the theme of TV dramas. In the first few months of 2019 the BBC Radio 4 drama *The Ferryhill Philosophers* grappled with the notion of what is the *self* that may or may not be destroyed by dementia. In an episode entitled 'Psychological continuity and the waterfall of self' the protagonists discuss whether there is such a thing as a *self* that constitutes what we are. According to the philosophers mentioned in this programme, John Locke and David Hulme, what makes a person today the same as the person of yesterday is 'psychological continuity'. There is no one thing that constitutes the *self*. We are a collection of memories, beliefs and feelings, 'a bundle of stuff' that has made us what we were in the past and still are. The father in the drama, who develops Alzheimer's, 'is still my dad', says the character Hermione. He still loves bagpipe music, sometimes he recognises his daughter and remembers very clearly episodes of their life together as a young father to a restless teenager. What he seems to have lost is the skill to make sequential links to his past. Like my own mother, he seems to see film shots in his mind's eye and he assumes that he had something to do with these pictures.

The question of whether 'the person is still there' was discussed on the *Start the Week* programme with Andrew Marr on BBC Radio 4 on Monday 8 April 2019. Here contributors to the discussion included the author Nicci Gerrard, who has written a memoir of her father's later life living with Alzheimer's,[60] and the science writer and broadcaster Sue Armstrong, who has written about the science of aging.[61] It was agreed during this discussion that 'even in later stages [of Alzheimer's] people can be reached'. The question that permeated the discussion was: is there a difference, in the mind disabled by Alzheimer's, between having a continuing presence of the self and having a continuing sense of the self? That is, is the Alzheimer's mind aware of feelings and needs?

We can sense from these two examples that we are becoming increasingly aware that we must alter the way we view dementia. This has to start by telling the people indirectly affected by this condition – the families of those displaying symptomatic behaviours and eventually diagnosed with declining mental abilities – that their mother/father/uncle/grandmother is still there. We must learn to reach into the deep recesses of the minds of people with this syndrome by altering the way we communicate with them. It was very sad listening to the daughter of the author Wendy Mitchell (talking on Radio 4 *Woman's Hour* on 2 April 2019) describe how much her

---

[60] Nicci Gerrard (2019). *What Dementia Teaches Us About Love*. Allen Lane.
[61] Sue Armstrong (2019). *The Science of How and Why We Age*. Bloomsbury Sigma.

mother's personality had changed and how she grieved for the previous person that her mother had been. It was very poignant to hear that her mother was present in that interview listening to her daughter saying how much she grieved for her lost mother. How incredibly sad. To grieve for a mother who still lives.

If a mother has a heart attack, she becomes unable to continue life in the same tenor as before. A daughter helps her mother make adjustments to her physical life. She cannot run miles any more as she had done all her life, but she can walk. If a mother breaks a wrist in a fall, she may not regain the quality of movement that she had before the fall: writing by hand may become slower and more laboured but a tablet will easily replace pen and paper that had previously been favoured by the mother. If a mother has a mild stroke some part of her brain will have been damaged that affects her linguistic ability to make sentences and she becomes angry and frustrated. Gradually it becomes obvious that other mental skills have been impaired by the stroke. She cannot remember her way home, as happens to Alice in the novel *Still Alice* by Lisa Genova. The necessary adjustments in this context are much harder to make because they require us to create a completely new and different world based on unfamiliar mindsets. But first of all, we must not consider that our mother has gone. She is there with us. She is broken in some way. But she is still our mother. She is not demented.

Support the manifesto

Let us reconceptualise dementia together:

1. **Abolish the word dementia.**
2. **Stop saying that the person that we knew 'has gone'.**
3. **Rethink the concept of time and space in the disabled mind.**
4. **Learn how to sustain meaningful conversations with Amelesians.**

Please visit https://amelsia.com and register your support for this approach if anything in this manifesto has touched you in any way at all.

Please feel free to contact me:

minadrever@aol.com

minadrever@amelesia.com

Appendix 1

ICD-11 – Dementia list – WHO – version: 04/2019

Each disease and/or condition is a subcategory of a parent group of diseases.

Dementia belongs to the group of neurocognitive disorders that in turn comes under the category 06 Mental, behavioural or neurodevelopmental disorders.

This implies a hierarchy of diseases each causing 'dementia' = madness.

Words in all capitals in the table are my emphasis.

Total diseases listed	Disease WHO code	Disease name	Parent disease category: each with code and name
1.	6D80	Dementia DUE to Alzheimer disease	06 Mental, behavioural or neurodevelopmental disorders • Neurocognitive disorders ▸ Dementia » 6D80 dementia due to Alzheimer disease • Dementia
	i. 6D80.0	Dementia DUE to Alzheimer disease with early onset (before age 65)	06 Mental, behavioural or neurodevelopmental disorders
	ii. 6D80.1	Dementia DUE to Alzheimer disease with late onset (from age 65)	06 Mental, behavioural or neurodevelopmental disorders
	iii. 6D80.Z	Dementia DUE to Alzheimer disease, onset unknown or unspecified	06 Mental, behavioural or neurodevelopmental disorders
2.	6D81	Dementia DUE to cerebrovascular disease	
3.	6D82	Dementia DUE to Lewy body disease	06 Mental, behavioural or neurodevelopmental disorders
4.	6D83	Frontotemporal dementia	06 Mental, behavioural or neurodevelopmental disorders
	6D84	Dementia DUE to psychoactive substances including medications	06 Mental, behavioural or neurodevelopmental disorders
5.	6D84.0	Dementia DUE to alcohol	06 Mental, behavioural or neurodevelopmental disorders

6.	6D84.1	Dementia DUE to use of sedatives, hypnotics or anxiolytics	06 Mental, behavioural or neurodevelopmental disorders
7.	6D84.2	Dementia DUE to use of volatile inhalants	06 Mental, behavioural or neurodevelopmental disorders
8.	6D84.Y	Dementia DUE to other specified substance	06 Mental, behavioural or neurodevelopmental disorders
	6D85	Dementia DUE to diseases classified elsewhere	06 Mental, behavioural or neurodevelopmental disorders
9.	6D85.0	Dementia DUE to Parkinson disease	06 Mental, behavioural or neurodevelopmental disorders
10.	6D85.1	Dementia DUE to Huntington disease	06 Mental, behavioural or neurodevelopmental disorders
11.	6D85.3	Dementia DUE to human immunodeficiency virus	06 Mental, behavioural or neurodevelopmental disorders
12.	6D85.4	Dementia DUE to multiple sclerosis	06 Mental, behavioural or neurodevelopmental disorders
13.	6D85.5	Dementia DUE to prion disease	06 Mental, behavioural or neurodevelopmental disorders
14.	.6		06 Mental, behavioural or neurodevelopmental disorders
15.	.Y		06 Mental, behavioural or neurodevelopmental disorders
16.	.Z		06 Mental, behavioural or neurodevelopmental disorders
17.	6D85.8	Dementia DUE to pellagra	06 Mental, behavioural or neurodevelopmental disorders
18.	6D85.9	Dementia DUE to Down syndrome	06 Mental, behavioural or neurodevelopmental disorders

Are the disturbances below (19–29) classified as diseases? Or symptomatic of diseases? It is confusing.

	6D86	Behavioural or psychological disturbances in dementia	06 Mental, behavioural or neurodevelopmental disorders
19.	6D86.0	Psychotic symptoms in dementia	06 Mental, behavioural or neurodevelopmental disorders
20.	6D86.1	Mood symptoms in dementia	06 Mental, behavioural or neurodevelopmental disorders
21.	6D86.2	Anxiety symptoms in dementia	06 Mental, behavioural or neurodevelopmental disorders
22.	6D86.3	Apathy in dementia	06 Mental, behavioural or neurodevelopmental disorders
23.	6D86.4	Agitation in dementia	06 Mental, behavioural or neurodevelopmental disorders
24.	6D86.5	Disinhibition in dementia	06 Mental, behavioural or neurodevelopmental disorders
25.	6D86.6	Wandering in dementia	06 Mental, behavioural or neurodevelopmental disorders
26.	6D86.Z	Behavioural or psychological disturbances in dementia, unspecified	06 Mental, behavioural or neurodevelopmental disorders
27.	6D8Z	Dementia, unknown or unspecified cause	06 Mental, behavioural or neurodevelopmental disorders
28.	6A02	Autism spectrum disorder	06 Mental, behavioural or neurodevelopmental disorders
29.	6A02.3	Autism spectrum disorder with disorder of intellectual development and with impaired functional language	06 Mental, behavioural or neurodevelopmental disorders

30.	8A00.25	Post traumatic Parkinsonism	08 Diseases of the nervous system
	8A06	Myoclonic disorders	08 Diseases of the nervous system
31.	8A06.Y	Other specified myoclonic disorders	08 Diseases of the nervous system
32.	8A60	Epilepsy DUE to structural or metabolic conditions or disease	08 Diseases of the nervous system
33.	8A60.3	Epilepsy DUE to dementia	08 Diseases of the nervous system
34.	8E4A	Paraneoplastic or autoimmune disorders of the nervous system	08 Diseases of the nervous system
35.	8E4A.0	Paraneoplastic or autoimmune disorders of the central system, brain or spinal cord	08 Diseases of the nervous system
36.	8B60	Motor neuron disease	08 Diseases of the nervous system
37.	8B60.5	Amyotrophic lateral sclerosis-Plus	08 Diseases of the nervous system
38.	1A60.3	Late congenital neurosyphilis	01 Certain infectious or parasitic diseases
39.	1A62.01	Symptomatic late neurosyphilis	01 Certain infectious or parasitic diseases
40.	1A62.0	Neurosyphilis	01 Certain infectious or parasitic diseases
41.	5B5A.Y	Other specified vitamin B1 deficiency	05 Endocrine, nutritional or metabolic diseases
42.	5B5A	Vitamin B1 deficiency	05 Endocrine, nutritional or metabolic diseases
43.	5B5E	Folate deficiency	05 Endocrine, nutritional or metabolic diseases
44.	8A001Y	Other specified atypical parkinsonism	08 Diseases of the nervous system
45.	8A00.1	Atypical parkinsonism	08 Diseases of the nervous system
46.	8A00	Parkinsonism	08 Diseases of the nervous system
47.	8A07.Y	Other specified movement disorder	08 Diseases of the nervous system

48.	8A07	Certain specified movement disorder	08 Diseases of the nervous system
49.	8E02.0	Genetic Creutzfeldt-Jakob disease	08 Diseases of the nervous system
50.	8E02	Genetic prior disease	08 Diseases of the nervous system
51.	SD86	Dementia disorder (TM1 – traditional medicine disorders)	26 Supplementary chapter traditional medicines conditions – Module 1
52.	8A20	Alzheimer disease	08 Diseases of the nervous system
53.	8B22.3	Isolated cerebral amyloid angiopathy	08 Diseases of the nervous system
54.	8B22	Certain specified cerebrovascular diseases	08 Diseases of the nervous system
55.	LD27,0Y	Other specified ectodermal dysplasia syndromes	20 Developmental anomalies
56.	LD27.0	Ectodermal dysplasia syndromes	20 Developmental anomalies

Observations

WHO gives six broad categories of diseases that cause dementia:

1. 06 Mental, behavioural or neurodevelopmental disorders
2. 08 Diseases of the nervous system
3. 01 Certain infectious or parasitic diseases
4. 05 Endocrine, nutritional or metabolic diseases
5. 26 Supplementary chapter traditional medicines conditions – Module 1
6. 20 Developmental anomalies

Total 'dementia' conditions in each category

06 Mental, behavioural or neurodevelopmental disorders	29 + 3 Alzheimer subcategories
08 Diseases of the nervous system	18
01 Certain infectious or parasitic diseases	3
05 Endocrine, nutritional or metabolic diseases	3
26 Supplementary chapter traditional medicines conditions – Module 1	1 ++++ Traditional medicines? How many?
20 Developmental anomalies	2 ++++ Developmental anomalies? How many?
Total	**53 AT LEAST +** 1 large category of traditional medicines 1 large category of developmental anomalies

At least 53+ conditions that cause dementia? Is this right?

Will diagnoses grow exponentially as more diseases are identified to cause similar symptoms?

Acknowledgements

Many people have contributed to the realisation of the work in this manifesto and, it is no false modesty on my part to say, without them, there would not be a manifesto. Without them, I would not have developed this strong urgency that I feel, that the world needs to change its idea of 'dementia'.

There is no hierarchy. I could not have done any of this work without the full commitment from and belief in me by Sue King, until September 2021 the manager at Redbond Lodge residential care home in Great Dunmow, Essex. She wants this to happen.

The headteacher, Chris Townsend, and the deputy headteacher, Karen Megahey, of Felsted School, near Great Dunmow, embraced my project with enthusiasm. The sixth form students who participated in the pilot training programme were amazing. They loved it. Thank you. Their role has been pivotal.

Ruth Saunders, a fellow linguist and great friend, considered this manifesto to be 'masterful'. Another friend, Wendy Bowden, found it 'strangely comforting', as she faced the prospect of her husband's developing Lewy body disease.

I have found staunch support in my friend Dr Saroj Cheema, a geriatric psychiatrist specialising in dementia. She believes that the word 'dementia' diminishes people.

My husband, Angus, my son, Jonathan, my son's partner, Lucy: unstinting belief and their continual urge to 'go for it'.

Margaret Hunter, of Daisy Editorial, has conducted an incredibly forensic editing of this book. Thank you, Margaret.

Thank you all.

Any mistakes in interpreting the literature research are my responsibility.

Printed in Great Britain
by Amazon